Do Not Quit, Quinn!

by Evelyn Ruiz

Target Skill Consonants Qq/kw/, Yy/y/
High-Frequency Words come, where

PEARSON

Scott
Foresman

Quinn, come here.
Look what Dad got.
It is for you.

Jump on it, Quinn.
You will like it.
It is fun.

Quinn can not go.
Do not quit, Quinn.
You can do it.

Quinn can not get it to go yet.

Do not quit, Quinn.

You can do it.

Look at Quinn go.

He can jump up and go!

He can do it.

Did Quinn get it?
Yes, he got it.
Look at him go.

Where will you go, Quinn?

Come with me, Dad.

Can we get a hot dog?